JOSH'S EXPEDITION

For Hannah with love
M.N

JOSH'S

EXPEDITION

Written by Margaret Nash

Illustrated by Sue Broadley

RED FOX

'I'm going on an expedition,' said Josh, one sunny morning.

'Well keep in the back garden,' said his mother,
who was busy looking for her watch.

Josh shuffled into his expedition clothes,
waved a wild goodbye and jumped down the steps.

He landed on top of a tiger's footprint
and flattened it.

He followed the footprints through the swamp,

round the waterhole…

and into the deepest part of the jungle.
There the tiger prints stopped.
Josh stopped too.

He heard a rustle. Two stripy ears, the colour of
gravy and marmalade appeared. Two eyes,
the colour of syrup appeared.

A nose, the colour of earth appeared.
The tiger roared.

Josh ran and ran and ran.

He ran to a tree and scrambled up its twisty branches.

He peeped down through slatted hands.
There was no tiger – it had gone thank goodness.
It was nowhere to be seen.

Sunshine was searching the jungle with long thin fingers.
It glossed the leaves and lit the insides of bushes.

Then it built a block of gold so bright,
it outsparkled everything in the jungle.
Josh wanted the block of gold more than anything
he could remember wanting. But what about the tiger?
The block of gold winked at him.

Josh climbed carefully down the tree.

He crept across the path.

He pushed through the bushes.

He snatched the sunshine and then…

He saw a shadow.

Josh turned and dashed indoors.

He pushed the block of gold
into Mummy's hand.

Mummy gasped, 'My Watch!'

She hugged Josh and danced him round the room.

Then they all had gooey stew for dinner and it smelled so good, guess who sprang onto the windowsill?

Yes, it was the tiger with the gravy and marmalade striped ears!